The Hungry Duckling

A Little Animal Adventure

The Hungry Duckling

Written by Claude Clément
Adapted by Deborah Kovacs
Illustrations by Marcelle Geneste

Published by The Reader's Digest Association Limited
London ❖ New York ❖ Sydney ❖ Montreal

'What a warm spring we're having!' said Mother Duck. 'I'd love to cool off in the water.'

'Then why not have a swim?' replied her friend, Mother Hen. 'I'll sit on your egg for you. I'm just waiting for my own to hatch.'

'Oh, thank you!' cried Mother Duck. 'I'll be back soon.' And she waddled off to the pond for a short swim.

That's how – a few minutes later – a little duckling came to be born into a family of chicks.

Mother Duck was still swimming so Mother Hen began teaching her little chicks – and the duckling – how to walk up and down and stretch their little legs.

'What a funny waddle he has,' said one little chick, pointing to the duckling. 'He's got such big flat feet!'

'Ssh,' said Mother Hen. 'Don't be rude! He is a little duckling, not a hen chick like the rest of you. If you visit the duck pond, you will see that all ducks waddle like that.'

All the little ones were hungry so Mother Hen began to show them how to peck up the tasty grain spread on the ground. The chicks pecked and pecked until they were full. But the duckling's bill was too big and round to pick up the tiny grains.

Poor duckling. He was starving! 'What can I eat?' he asked his little chick friends. 'It's easy for you to peck. You've got little pointed beaks.'

But they couldn't help. So, feeling very sorry for himself, the duckling waddled away.

The first creature he met was a snail. 'I'm so hungry,' said the duckling. 'Can I eat you?'

'Oh dear, no,' said the snail. 'Think about it for a moment. You would simply break your teeth on my very tough shell. Now that's not a good idea, is it?'

And the snail moved slowly on his way. So did the duckling – looking very sad and feeling even hungrier. What was he to do?

After a while, he said to himself, 'That snail was a rogue. Ducks don't have teeth. Oh, how silly I am!'

But the cunning snail was nowhere to be seen. A little later, the duckling met a small green frog.

'I'd love to gobble her up,' thought the duckling but the clever frog guessed what he was thinking and quickly replied …

'Don't even think of it, my little friend. I'd dance and leap around so much in your tummy, you'd get hiccups.'

And while the duckling thought about this, the frog leapt off quickly across the meadow.

Before long, the hungry little duckling reached the pond. There was Mother Duck, just finishing her swim.

'My little duckling!' she quacked in surprise. 'You hatched early. Jump in and learn how to swim.'

'No, I won't,' said the duckling crossly. 'I don't want to get wet! I've nothing to dry myself with.'

His mother laughed. 'You don't need a towel. You've got waterproof feathers. Come on. You'll see. Swimming is great for ducks.'

The duckling groaned. 'No, I'm too hungry. I *must* find some food.' And he started to waddle away.

At that moment a little kingfisher, who was watching from a nearby tree, shouted out, 'You're just scared. You're just chicken!' and dived into the pond.

'No, I'm not. I'm a duck!' shouted the duckling. He was so angry he dived straight in after the kingfisher.

Under the water the duckling watched the kingfisher gobbling up little minnows and worms from the bottom of the pond. His tummy began to rumble. He was so very, very hungry.

'Try some,' called the kingfisher.

So the little duckling tried some. 'They're delicious!' he exclaimed. 'I'm so glad I've discovered what ducks eat.'

'Bravo!' said Mother Duck. 'You're a great little diver. I am so proud of my little duckling.'

At the end of the day, they waddled back to the farmyard together, full of food and ready for bed.

'I'm glad you're not a hungry duckling anymore,' said Mother Duck.

'I'm a sleepy duckling now,' yawned her little son.

So Mother Duck tucked him under her warm wing and said, 'good night.'

All about ... DUCKS

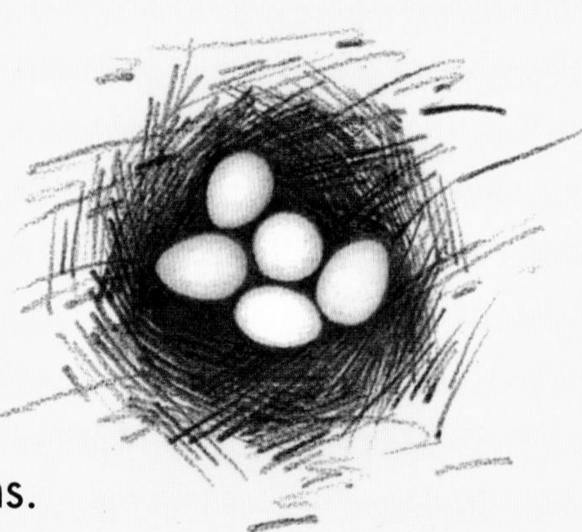

MINDING THE NEST
Duck eggs must be kept very warm, so a mother duck can leave them only for short periods of time while she eats or swims.

DUCK DINNERS
Ducks dive into the water to look for their favourite food – tadpoles, small frogs, worms and little fish.

FACT FILE

WATERPROOF COATS
Duck feathers are covered with a fine layer of waterproof grease. These special feathers help ducks to stay afloat, so they can swim for a long time without getting tired.

Did you know?

SUPER SWIMMERS

Ducks love water. That's why they will often leave the farmyard to go and splash about in ponds.

Thanks to their webbed feet they are very good swimmers.

WAG TAILS

Ducklings have a funny way of walking. When they pick up their flat little feet, their tails waggle from side to side. This helps them to keep their balance.

BIG BILLS

Ducks have broad beaks called 'bills'. At the edge of their bills are ridges that filter the water they drink.

The Hungry Duckling is a Little Animal Adventures book
published by Reader's Digest Young Families, Inc.
by arrangement with Éditions Nathan, Paris, France

Written by Claude Clément
Adapted by Deborah Kovacs
Illustrations by Marcelle Geneste
Notebook artwork © Paul Bommer

This edition was adapted and published in 2008 by
The Reader's Digest Association Limited
11 Westferry Circus, Canary Wharf, London E14 4HE

We are committed to both the quality of our products
and the service we provide to our customers.
We value your comments, so please feel free to contact us on
08705 113366 or via our website at:
www.readersdigest.co.uk
If you have any comments or suggestions about the
content of our books, you can contact us at:
gbeditorial@readersdigest.co.uk

Printed in China

Book code: 637-003 UP0000-3
ISBN: 978 0 276 44233 9